To:

From:

Published by Hallmark Books,
a division of Hallmark Cards, Inc.,
Kansas City, MO 64141
Visit us on the Web at www.Hallmark.com.

"Monster Mash"
© 1962 Written by Bobby Pickett & Leonard Capizzi
Published by FSMGI (IMRO), Gary S. Paxton Publications
(BMI), & Capizzi Music Co. (BMI)
Rights for FSMGI (IMRO) & Gary S. Paxton Publications (BMI)
administered by State One Music America (BMI)

Characters based on the illustrations by Sarah Anderson

Editor: Megan Langford
Art Director: Kevin Swanson
Designer: Mark Voss
Production Artist: Dan C. Horton

ISBN: 978-1-59530-304-2

BOK6165

Printed and bound in China
APR10

THE MONSTER MASH

ILLUSTRATED BY MARIA SARRIA

GIFT BOOKS
from Hallmark

I was working in the lab late one night,
when my eyes beheld an eerie sight.
For my monster from his slab began to rise
and suddenly to my surprise . . .

He did the monster mash!

THE MONSTER MASH!

It was a graveyard smash!

HE DID THE MASH!

It caught on in a flash.

HE DID THE MASH!

He did the monster mash!

From my laboratory
in the castle east
to the master bedroom
where the vampires feast,
the ghouls all came
from their humble abodes
to get a jolt
from my electrodes!

They did the mash!

THEY DID THE MONSTER MASH!

The monster mash!

It was a graveyard smash.
THEY DID THE MASH!

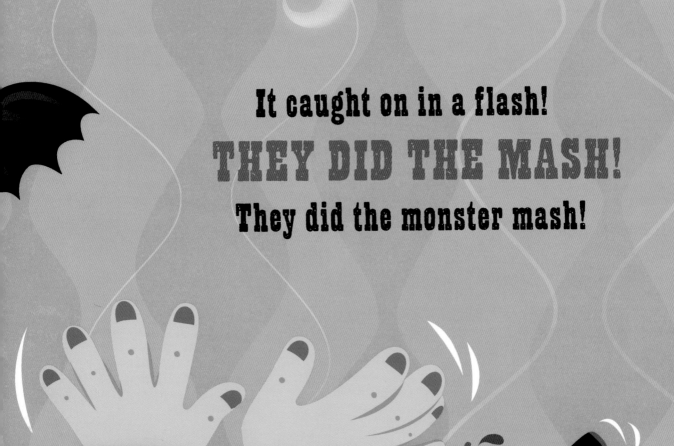

It caught on in a flash!
THEY DID THE MASH!
They did the monster mash!

The zombies were having fun—
the party had just begun!
The guests included Wolf Man,
Dracula, and his son.

The scene was rockin',
all were digging the sounds.
Igor on chains,
backed by his baying hounds.

The coffin-bangers were about to arrive
with their vocal group,
"THE CRYPT-KICKER FIVE."

They played the mash!
THEY PLAYED THE MONSTER MASH!
The monster mash!
It was a graveyard smash!
THEY PLAYED THE MASH!
It caught on in a flash.
THEY PLAYED THE MASH!
They played the monster mash!

Out from his coffin, Drac's voice did ring.
Seems he was troubled by just one thing.

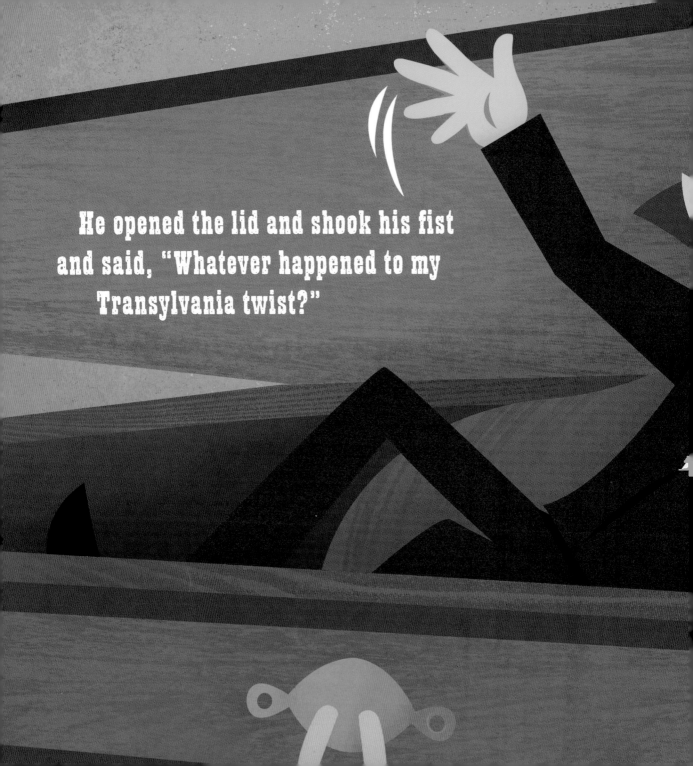

He opened the lid and shook his fist and said, "Whatever happened to my Transylvania twist?"

It's now the mash!
IT'S NOW THE MONSTER MASH!
The monster mash!
And it's a graveyard smash!
IT'S NOW THE MASH!
It caught on in a flash.
IT'S NOW THE MASH!
It's now the monster mash!

Now everything's cool,
Drac's a part of the band.
And my monster mash
is the hit of the land!
For you, the living,
this mash was meant, too.
When you get to my door,
tell them Boris sent you!

Then you can mash!
THEN YOU CAN MONSTER MASH!
The monster mash!
And do my graveyard smash!
THEN YOU CAN MASH!
You'll catch on in a flash.
THEN YOU CAN MASH!
Then you can monster mash!

HAVE YOU ENJOYED THIS BOOK?
WE WOULD LOVE TO HEAR FROM YOU.

Hallmark Book Feedback
P.O. Box 419034
Mail Drop 215
Kansas City, MO 64141

booknotes @ hallmark.com